AN ANTHOLOGY OF

OLD ENGLISH POETRY